The Amazing Mumford Forgets the Magic Words!

written by Patricia Thackray

illustrated by Normand Chartier

This educational book was created in cooperation with the Children's Television Workshop, producers of Sesame Street. Children do not have to watch the television show to benefit from this book. Workshop revenues from this product will be used to help support CTW educational projects.

A SESAME STREET BOOK

Published by Western Publishing Company, Inc. in conjunction with Children's Television Workshop. © 1979 Children's Television Workshop. The Amazing Mumford and other Muppet characters © 1979 Muppets, Inc. All rights reserved. Produced in U.S.A. Sesame Street® and the Sesame Street sign are trademarks and service marks of Children's Television Workshop. The Amazing Mumford is a trademark of Muppets, Inc. GOLDEN®, A LITTLE GOLDEN BOOK®, and GOLDEN PRESS® are trademarks of Western Publishing Company, Inc. No part of this book may be reproduced or copied in any form without written permission from the publisher.